MW00632786

This "Gift" Belongs To

_____

"All good giving and every perfect gift
is from above, coming down from the Father"

—James 1:17

To all the children of the world:

Our joy for today,

Our hope for tomorrow.

Copyright 2012
Published 2013 by

PO Box 13, Warrenton, VA 20188
www.MysticalRoseInspirations.com

ISBN: 978-0-9857405-0-4
Library of Congress Control Number: 2012912548

This product is compliant with CPSIA 2008, Printed in China.
Illustrated by David W. Luebbert.
www.Lueb-Art.com

To Order:
540-364-2841 or 1-888-965-ROSE (7673)
www.GiftofaServant.com.

GIFT OF A SERVANT

BY TAMARA AMOS

Illustrations by David W. Luebbert
Published 2013 by

Mystical Rose

ABOUT THE STORY:

"When I was growing up, my parents made great sacrifices to provide for our family, raising their seven children to love God and to be good Christians. My father loved Christmas! It was the one time of year when he could unrestrainedly lavish love upon us in the form of gifts. Every December, he would become as jolly as an elf with a twinkle in his eye- the entire household would be filled with excitement and anticipation,Christmas music, decorations, and home-made crafts! The coldest blizzard couldn't have chilled the warmth of a Christmas morning, as we joyously exchanged gifts we had lovingly chosen for each other and unwrapped mysterious packages left for us in the night by our dear friend, Santa Claus.

"When I was sixteen, I asked my dad what he wanted for his birthday. His answer surprised me: "I would like for someone to write about how people can come to know God through Santa Claus." What an idea! The more I thought about it, the more I could see the parallel. Children, especially, relate to this loving saint who knows them each personally and dedicates his entire life to making and giving them gifts. How like our heavenly Father he is! And how well he imitates Christ. Parents sometimes worry that children will misinterpret the emphasis that is placed on Santa Claus at Christmas time, but we never had that problem. We understood that he is a servant of God. On our birthdays, we receive gifts, but on God's birthday, He sends Santa Claus to give us gifts so we know how much He loves us!

"Years later, I was inspired to write Gift of a Servant. I pray that through it, you experience the unfathomable love of God that comes to us disguised as ordinary people and shines through us when we live lives of extraordinary love."

—Tamara Amos

"Intense love does not measure,
it just gives."

—Mother Teresa

A Christmas Eve not long ago,
I sat alone at my window
people-watching,
but I was mostly
gazing bleakly at the snow.

I don't hesitate to say
that on that blustering Advent day,
though I longed for cheer,
for peace to adhere,
the Christmas spirit was far away.

As the hurried shoppers all passed by,
A gleam of madness in their eyes,
I couldn't help
but ask myself
if Santa Claus was the reason why.

Mirrored in a candle stick
that had lost the light upon its wick,
my sad heart mourned
a friend of yore;
for what had become of Good St. Nick?

I remembered him a childhood dream,
who for me once had seemed
the essence of
Christmas love,
so pure and good, generous and holy.

But this new man upon the signs,
on every TV and every mind
was not the same,
did not contain
the peace and joy of that same kind.

For hysteria pervaded the hearts of men:
Buy! Buy! Buy! Spend! Spend! Spend!
A cultural norm
in a commercial form
had replaced our good and holy friend.

Indignation rose within me,
overflowed and re-entered in me.
Who was this Claus
who was the cause
of this superficial frenzy?!

My mind began to devise a plan,
face-to-face to tell this man
the harm he's done
to God's own Son.
His resignation I would demand.

All the night I did not sleep—
a crusader's vigil I did keep.
My anger burned...
and then I heard
the sound above of reindeer feet!

For a moment I was paralyzed
with the anticipation of old Christmas nights.
The child within me
stirred excitedly
and I forgot all that I had devised.

I stood there waiting in awe and fear
those soot black boots for to appear.
Then from thin air,
he materialized there-
crimson red suit and snow white beard!

His eyes of blue saw me then
and awkwardly, I began
to remember
my righteous anger,
my mission for my fellow man.

"Santa Claus, what have you wrought?
Anxiety is our Christmas lot.
Christmas spirit?
We cannot feel it!
Our peace is gone and it's all your fault!

"And our poor kids, what do they have,
but materialism to drive them mad?!
The toys, the stuff,
I've had enough!
Poor Christ in Heaven must be so sad!

"Good St. Nick, I do implore;
these aren't the simple days of yore.
Men now-a-days
are in a craze.
Enough is not, they must have more.

"So, if you have a spark within
of pity for the little children,
You'll take your leave
without retrieve
and give God's birthday back to him!"

The old man heaved a breath so long;
one that knew a world of wrong.
And in that sigh,
I heard the cry
of suffering so great he'd taken on.

"The children..."was all that he intoned,
not so much word as much as moan.
"Take my hand
and understand
that your concern for them is not alone."

He reached out his welcoming hand to me
as I stood there accusingly.
Though strong my grudge,
a gentle nudge
drove me the gesture to appease.

I took his hand, my eyes met his,
but so much more – my soul, that is.
And a symbolic vision
of his mission
flashed before me in powerful images.

I saw a sea of children crying:
abused, neglected, ill, and dying.
So much pain
did remain
for these little ones justice was denying.

Then a man came forth to them
from the sky to earth again:
Christ the Lord!
The Father's Word
rushed to them with outstretched hands.

But, men appeared and held them back.
"Don't let them go. That man is mad!"
Others came
and did the same.
"The Son of God is too good for that!"

He raised His voice authoritatively,
"Let the children come to Me
and do not hinder,
for remember:
My kingdom belongs to such as these."

The scene that I saw next held joy,
for every girl and ever boy
stood 'round the Lord
who did reward
their childlike innocence with love unalloyed.

He smiled at one and healed another,
an apple for him, a kiss for the other.
They laughed and played
all the day...
but what happened next, left them scared and befuddled.

The same men came and crucified
sweet Jesus right before their eyes.
"But, He loves us!"
the children chorused
as they rushed unto His side.

He gazed upon them lovingly
with grateful eyes, then made a plea:
"Who will go
and My love show
these little ones for whom My heart weeps?"

A hero emerged from the jeering crowd.
"Here I am," he said aloud,
with beard of white
and blue eyes bright,
in bold red suit stood proud.

"Hold My lambs within your heart.
From My mercy, let them never part.
Give gifts of love
from Heaven above,
so they know how precious to Me they are."

He held them 'til the savior died
and when the soldier pierced His side,
a ray of light
illumined the night
and on the head of this saint it came to abide.

An angel descended to lay a kiss
on the cheek of Good St. Nicholas,
and on him bestowed
God's grace to know
a long life to carry out His wish.

I came-to holding that age old hand
which God had blessed to hold His lambs.
With true remorse,
I said, "Of course!
Now I understand.

"Just as Jesus bore our shame,
it was on you I put the blame
for *our* sin
which let in
the materialism of our day."

The old man smiled and in his gaze,
I found the peace of long gone days.
Then suddenly,
he winked at me
and said, "The children cannot wait!"

He opened up his big brown sack;
bright, wrapped presents he unpacked:
'gifts of love
from Heaven above'
for my children who in nothing lacked.

He placed them carefully beneath the tree,
saying each name individually.
He generously filled
the stockings until
they overflowed with their favorite candy.

Tears streamed down my face when he
turned to say good-bye to me.
He reached out his hand;
to him I ran
and held him close to me.

"I love you, Santa Claus," I sobbed,
"and I want to help you do your job.
What can I do
to bring true
Christmas spirit back to the mob?"

I searched for wisdom in his face,
and the feeling of a warm embrace
encompassed my soul
as he retold
words meant for the whole human race:

"Hold His lambs within your heart.
From His mercy, let them never part.
Give gifts of love
from Heaven above,
so they know how precious to Him they are."

And as he turned to take his leave,
in his face, my heart perceived
what I'd missed before
–in but an instant or more–
the face of Christ looking back at me.

I fell down on my knees to pray,
to thank the Lord that holy day
for saints and men
our Father sends
to help us on our way.

Now, every day I stop and pause
to reflect upon God's good laws:

Love One

And Be Christ

Another

To Each Other

For that was my gift from Santa Claus.

"I live, no longer I, but Christ lives in me."

— Galatians 2:20

ABOUT THE AUTHOR

Tamara Amos was born July 21, 1976 to Brian and Michele Page in Virginia and grew up in many different countries. Over-seas, she taught English as a second language and worked in ministry. She earned her BA in Theology in 1997 and married Rob Amos in 1998. They have four children. She has since worked extensively in the fields of business, education, and ministry, developing programs that incorporate mind-body-soul methodology and creative learning experiences. She specializes in multi-dimensional education and bi-cerebral learning styles, ADD/ADHD advocacy, and holistic healing. She owns and operates Mystical Rose, a company dedicated to cultivating creative talent and inspiring positive solutions for an era of peace through inspirational publishing, products, and services.

Through inspirational publishing, products, and services, Mystical Rose aims to equip this generation with the power to co-create an era of peace by harnessing the unique gifts and surmounting the obstacles of our exciting, yet challenging time. All people are images of their creator and hold within themselves a limitless source of creativity, talent, and ingenuity. Mystical Rose seeks to help people discover their place in the world, cultivate their talents, and develop a cooperative spirit so that together we may solve the problems of our day and meet our potential, both as individuals and as a human family.

Visit us on our website to order Gift of a Servant or
to learn more about our products and services, including:

PRODUCTS	SERVICES
Inspirational Books & Merchandise	Author Services
Multi-Dimensional Educational Resources	Training Seminars
Multi-Media Church Resources	Good Will Ambassadorship
ADD/ADHD Resources & Products	& Awards Program
	Youth Leadership Program

Mystical Rose

www. MysticalRoseInspirations.com
PO Box 13
Warrenton, VA 20188
540-364-2841/1-888-965-ROSE